Classroom Approaches

No doubt many of us at sometime or other have carved out a breathing space by setting a creative writing task at a moment's notice. As a survival technique it is understandable but it is impossible to justify educationally.

'Creative Writing' has suffered badly from allegations of lack of clear objectives, woolly classroom organisation and lack of structure. In using the contents of this book we would therefore suggest the teacher considers a number of possible classroom techniques and organisational approaches.

Children are authors when engaged in Creative Writing. The creativity provides a unique character to the work not present in other aspects of English language work. It is important therefore to model the pupil activity on that of authors in general. In writing any piece we begin with an outline draft of the final objective. Ideas can be agreed and key vocabulary identified. The time devoted to such pre-planning will vary according to the age and ability of the writer but it ought to be there. It need not all be written, a dialogue with the teacher and /or other pupils will be of great benefit in many cases, allowing the child to verbalise ideas and in so doing to refine and clarify a plan of action. It is worth considering providing pupils with a notebook which is specifically for such planning purposes. The same book may contain the key words the child intends to use to introduce into the story. In many cases these may have been cross-checked either with an adult or using a dictionary.

Beware, however, that the trappings of authorship do not smother the central idea of what the child wants to say. Too much pre-planning with pupils who are not ready can turn off even the most enthusiastic. On occasions it is valid for a group of children to be given the same task. The identification of key words can then become a group activity. A suitable display (e.g. a word tree) can then be developed from which pupils will choose words appropriate to their own particular responses.

The Word Tree

Sheet 5 is a photocopy free sheet of a Word Tree. It can be used with any of the other sheets in this book in order to support the child's writing.

It can be used in a variety of ways:

By individuals planning their own writing.

By groups collaborating on a joint piece of writing.

By teachers/other adults to support children's writing.

By older children working with younger pupils.

By the teacher (enlarge the sheet to A3 for display).

By the teacher and child in a pupil file which builds up a range of vocabulary.

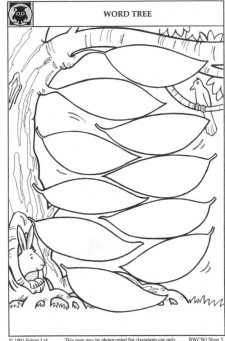

WORD TREE

ENGLISH KEY STAGE ONE

WRITING

LEVEL	STATEMENT OF ATTAINMENT	RELEVANT SHEETS
1	**Pupils should be able to:** a) use pictures, symbols or isolated letters, words or phrases to communicate meaning.	Applicable to all sheets
2	a) produce, independently, pieces of writing using complete sentences, some of them demarcated with capital letters and full stops or question marks.	To be encouraged at all times
	b) structure sequences of real or imagined events coherently in chronological accounts.	7 - 9, 23
	c) write stories showing an understanding of the rudiments of story structure by establishing an opening, characters, and one or more events.	9,10,20,22,26,36
	d) produce simple, coherent non-chronological writing.	19,20,22,26,36,38,38,40
3	a) produce, independently, pieces of writing using complete sentences, mainly demarcated with capital letters and full stops or question marks.	To be encouraged at all times
	b) shape chronological writing, beginning to use a wider range of sentence connectives than 'and' and 'then'.	15-17
	c) write more complex stories with detail beyond simple events and with a defined ending.	10,13,18,22,25,27,30,34,37,39
	d) produce a range of types of non-chronological writing.	35 - 38,40,46 - 48
	e) begin to revise and redraft in discussion with teacher, other adults or other children in the class, paying attention to the meaning and clarity as well as checking for matters such as correct and consistent use of tense and pronouns.	To be encouraged at all times

WORD TREE

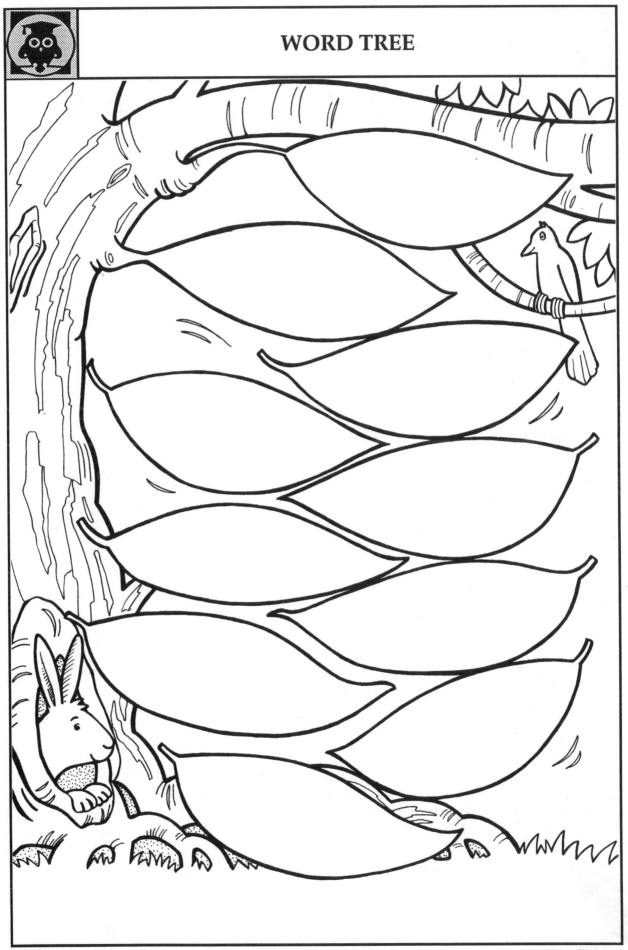

STRUCTURING AND SEQUENCING STORIES

We have chosen to introduce the theme of sequence and structure in story-telling through the use of traditional fairy tales which most children will have encountered. It is important that the children do know the rhymes/stories before embarking on these sheets.

The first two sheets relate to nursery rhymes which have clear beginnings, middles and ends.
The setting - Jack and Jill go up the hill
What happens? - They fall down
Outcome - Bed and repair work!

Throughout the section we would encourage the use by the teacher of words such as beginning, middle, end, characters, sequence. These can also be used to label written work in display.

Other rhymes and stories can be enjoyed, recited and acted out and the children can discuss the common structure of most stories.

Individual Sheets

Sheet 7 - Jack and Jill. The pictures provide a visual context to support the text. Some children will follow the visual sequence and will know by heart the rhyme but will need support in writing the ending.

Sheet 8 - Humpty Dumpty. This time the middle and the end are provided and discussion should focus on what is missing - the beginning. What would the rhyme be like if we didn't have the beginning?

Sheet 9 - Red Riding Hood. Sheets 7 and 8 have a set text which the child will have learned and then written down.

In this sheet the story will be known in terms of its narrative sequence but the actual words to be used are the child's own.

The Word Tree (Sheet 5) may be useful here to help with the spelling of key words as well as in generating a broad vocabulary. Illustrations will require extra sheets.

Sheet 10 - Night Time. Progression is found in two respects. The story is not traditional therefore there is no agreed narrative to follow but the design of the page encourages the writing of distinct middles and ends. This is also the first sheet where the children write two sections rather than one.

Sheets 11/12/13 - My Pal from Pluto. This comes in three sections. They are intended to be joined together for display. Each sheet provides a frame for the three parts of the story.

This can also lend itself to class/group story construction.

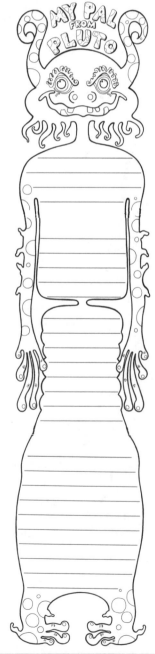

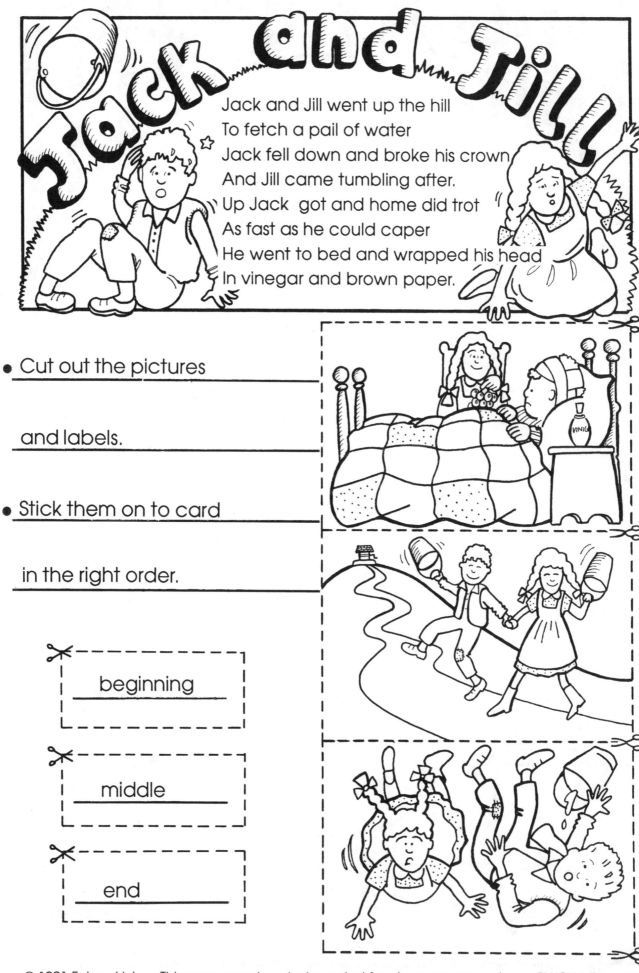

Jack and Jill

Jack and Jill went up the hill
To fetch a pail of water
Jack fell down and broke his crown
And Jill came tumbling after.
Up Jack got and home did trot
As fast as he could caper
He went to bed and wrapped his head
In vinegar and brown paper.

• Cut out the pictures

and labels.

• Stick them on to card

in the right order.

beginning

middle

end

HUMPTY DUMPTY

Humpty Dumpty had a great fall.

All the king's horses and all

the king's men couldn't put

Humpty together again.

Red Riding Hood

beginning

Little Red Riding Hood set

off to visit her Grandma.

Grandma lived in a

cottage on the far

side of the wood.

middle

Red Riding Hood met a wolf.

He asked her where she was

going. She told him and he ran into

the woods.

end

One night I heard a strange scratching noise.

I felt under my bed.

Night time

• Write the middle and end of this story.

BWCW1 Sheet 10

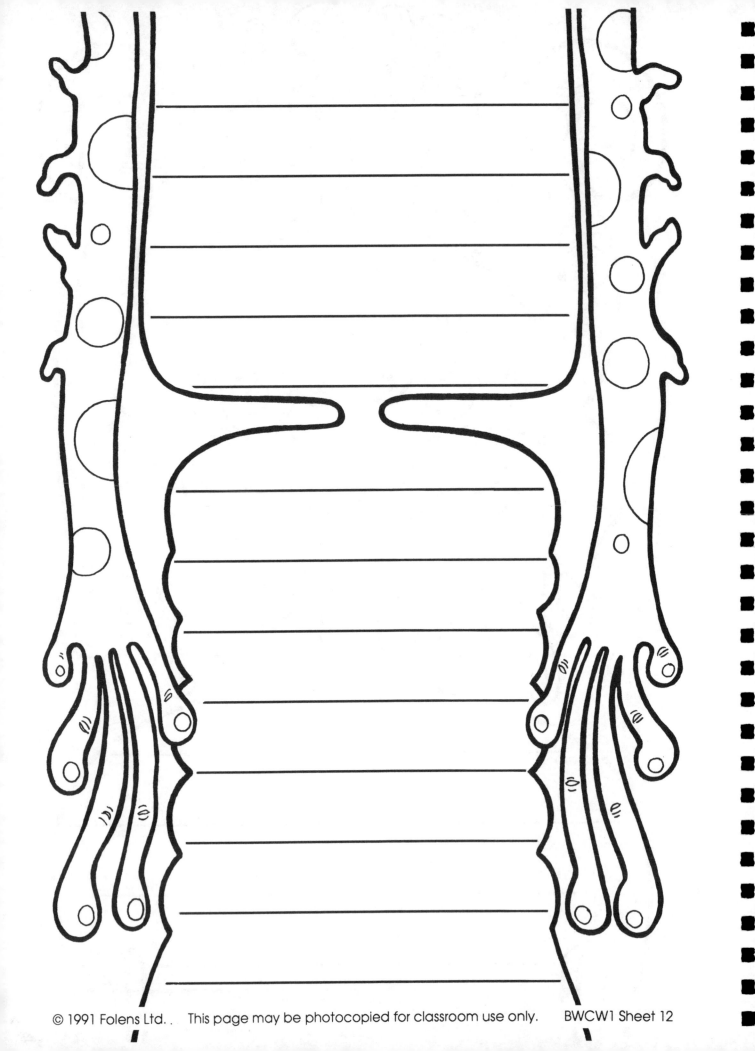

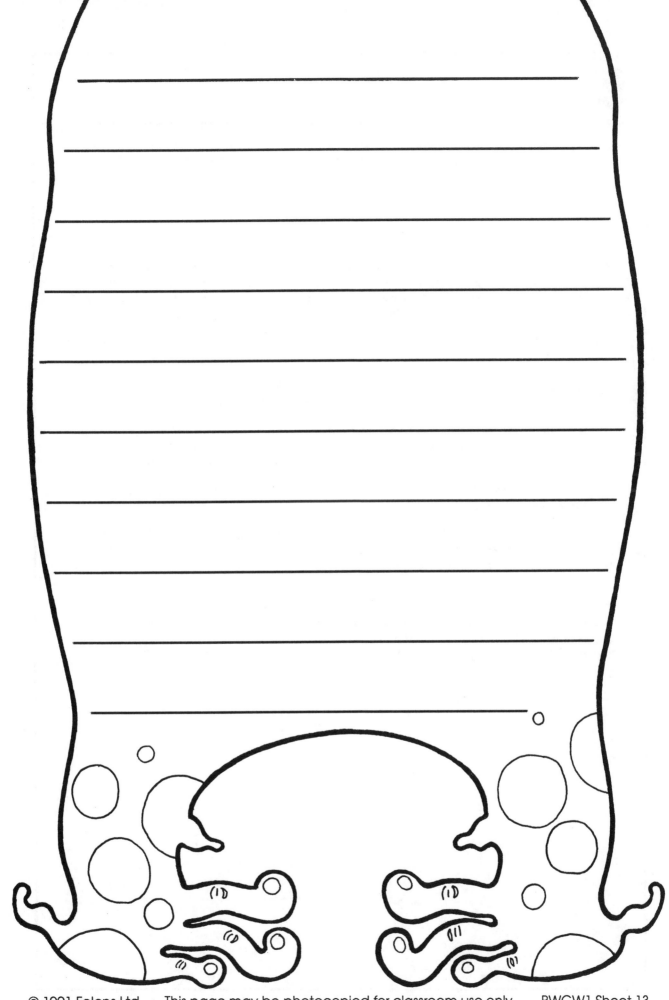

POINTS OF VIEW

We have attempted in this section to begin at a point which we feel is conceptually more appropriate for writing 'points of view'. Before including characters' points of view within a story it is valuble to take a single event or a picture and to explore viewpoints.

How would you feel? How do you think Charlotte felt? Why did Sita do/say that?

Individual Sheets

Sheet 15 - Pam's Penguin. The points of view are clearly identified with the different speakers through the use of speech bubbles. The picture provides a context and the speech bubbles contain cues as to the opinions of each speaker. The child has to look for reasons why each speaker responds as they do. There is a wide range of possible outcomes.

Sheet 16 - Fast Food. Textual cues are not provided for this sheet so the child needs to identify the action from the visual context.

Group discussion is important as an introduction to this sheet. Different children can be asked to identify with the various characters: 'How would they feel?' 'What would you reply if the teacher said...?'

Sheet 17 - Bedtime. Characters' points of view need not always be spoken. Children's writing can include people's thoughts as well as their words. This sheet has a range of possible outcomes and points of view. Discussion and writing can be further developed with a 'What happens next?' question.

Sheet 18 - Little Miss Muffet. Here the children are encouraged to examine all alternatives to the 'traditional' points of view.

Sheet 19 - Hey Diddle Diddle. The points of view expressed here are essentially defensive. Each offers an explanation for the events described in the rhyme. The children can think of other nursery rhymes and provide explanations for the actions described in them: Little Jack Horner / Little Boy Blue / Georgie Porgie, etc.

Sheet 20 - Great Excuses. Sheet 19 leads us to the final points of view - great excuses. Some of the least likeable characters from traditional stories are allowed to offer their own points of view and the children then consider similar explanations for other characters. This can be linked to the children's (and teachers!) own experiences of the bizarre and incredibly imaginative excuses advanced daily in schools.

Pam's Penguin

I'm not teaching him because
_____
_____
_____

I'd like to stay because
_____
_____

He has to stay
because
_____
_____
_____
_____

He can't sit there because
_____
_____

- Complete the speech bubbles.

Fast Food

● Write what you think each person is saying.

Bed time

It's time for bed

Complete the bubbles

Little Miss Muffet

One day I was busy weaving my web when

_____

_____

_____

_____

Hey Diddle Diddle

• Cut out the captions and stick them on the right picture.

Hey diddle diddle,

The cat and the fiddle,

The cow jumped over the moon.

The little dog laughed

To see such fun

And the dish ran away

With the spoon.

You hum it and I'll play it.

Someone tickled me.

I'm fed up with the cow jumping over me.

I'd rather have a fork.

GREAT EXCUSES

I was pushed.

An apple a day

Keeps the doctor away.

I only wanted to play

with the pigs.

We thought she'd be

warm by the fire.

● Now write captions and draw pictures for :-

Goldilocks   Goosey Gander

Rumplestiltskin   The Grand Old Duke of York

STORY TELLING

Elements of of structuring, sequencing and writing from points of view should be included in the stories children produce in this section.

We would suggest that a number of classroom strategies be considered when using these sheets. Although each sheet is designed to be completed by individuals there can be considerable advantage in developing a group or class story. The same illustration can serve as a starting point. Each child in turn contributes a single sentence to the narrative. The end result is a story in which each member of the group/class has a stake. Often these stories are of remarkable quality and the cross-fertilisation that occurs can be highly productive.

Individual story contributions can be produced in a 'children's weekly/monthly' in-house magazine. These are relatively easy to produce with the right software and have a real impact on the general quality of story writing. It is worth considering the use of some of these sheets in longer story format. The children can then chapterise their responses as they move towards more mature styles of writing.

Individual Sheets

Sheet 22 - Sky High. The children complete the whole story by drawing the fourth picture. Class discussion should centre around predictions of possible outcomes. More pictures can be drawn if the child wants to add a lengthy sequence.

The whole story should then be written in the child's own words. The word tree may prove of value for the specific vocabulary, e.g. engine, aeroplane, wing, etc.

Sheet 23 - Over The Edge. A single visual stimulus which may be seen as the middle of a chain of events. The story might therefore address the question of what has already happened to lead to this situation, what the points of view of the characters are and how the whole thing will end.

Sheet 24 - Budgie on the Loose. The story can be written by individuals but it also lends itself to group activity. Tell/write a happy ending - each child tells the happy ending from different points of view. The cat and the crow may have other ideas to those of the budgie. It is also valuable to debate the most likely outcome.

Sheet 25 - Pass it On. This is intended to be used for a group story. The whole story can be brainstormed by a group of children (use the Word Tree p.5 as a resource) and a writer is then nominated. Alternatively each individual contributes a sentence to the whole story, each sentence must take up from where the previous one ended.

This second option can be further developed by allowing the body of the story to be produced in this way with the final 3/4 lines being written by children working individually.

Sheet 26 - Shipwreck. Again this has great potential as a group activity. Individuals can choose their own six items and then discuss their choices in a group. The pros and cons of each can be explored (listening and speaking) and a shared list produced. Whether using the individual or the group list the choice imposes a discipline on the writing of 'my adventure'.

There are some interesting moral issues to be explored here. Do you abandon the cat in order to improve your chance of survival? Once the children have completed their stories they can discuss whether they would like to change their minds about their original choice - and how a different selection might have resulted in alternative outcomes.

Sheet 27 - You have three wishes. The children's imaginations will be fired when the teacher reads/tells some 'genie' stories and if the children have access to books/pictures depicting this kind of tale. The children then have carte blanche but they should be encouraged to link their choices to the actual outcomes. It is possible to set this sheet in the future and therefore to ask the children to use the future tense.

● Draw what happens next.

● Write a story to match the pictures.

- What happens next? _____

_____

_____

_____

_____

_____

_____

Budgie on the loose

- What happens next?

_____

_____

_____

_____

_____

_____

_____

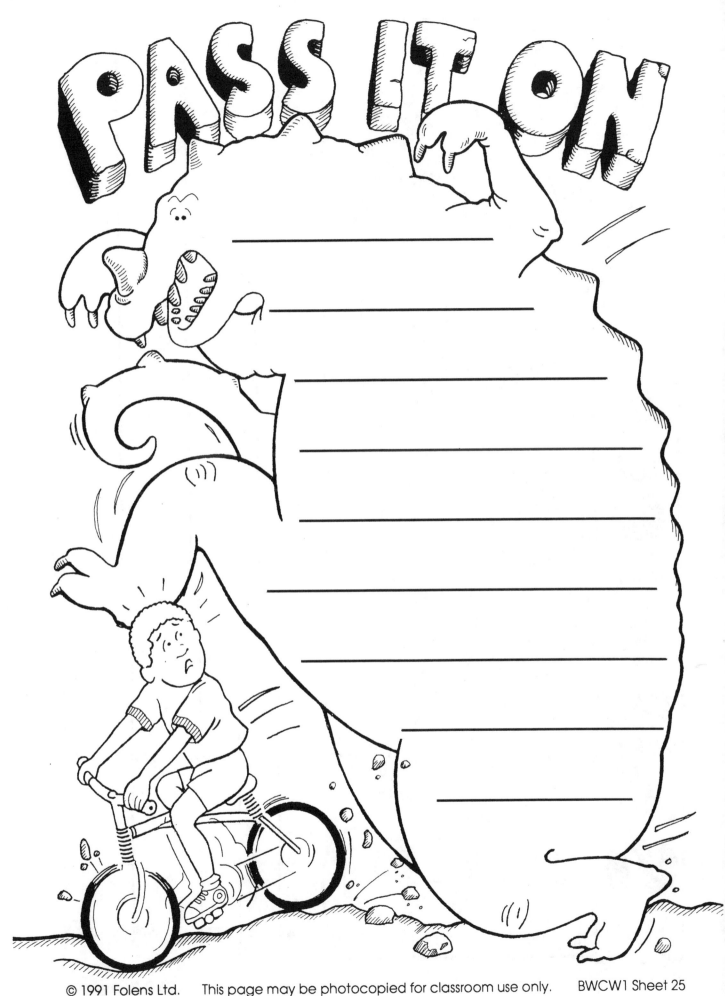

Shipwreck

My adventure

• Choose 6 items to

take with you

1 _____   4 _____

2 _____   5 _____

3 _____   6 _____

You have three wishes

What will you wish for?

Write what will happen if your wishes come true.

IMAGINATIVE/DESCRIPTIVE WRITING

This is the largest section in the book and is intended to provide a variety of stimuli which will allow a wide range of approaches.

It is useful to discuss with the children whether or not they will be in the story or whether they will simply be story tellers who do not actually feature in the narrative.

There is scope here for increasing complexity in the writing and in the characterisations.

Individual Sheets

Sheet 30 - Best Foot Forward. This is a sheet where the child will need to decide whether or not to be the subject of the story. The footwear reflects the real world but imaginations need not be constrained by such realism. Magical ballet shoes, rocket-propelled roller skates, etc., all open up great possibilities for imaginative writing.

The sheet can be used on a number of occasions, different footwear being chosen each time. Creativity can be further challenged if the children have to mix the footwear. One clown's shoe and a flipper could open up the possibility of an underwater circus!

Sheet 31 - On Top. This sheet consolidates No. 29. Role play can precede/supplement the activity. We feel it is important that children should not be constrained by gender from taking any of the hats and writing a story which includes themselves. The writing here can be based in realism or in flights of fancy.

Sheet 32 - Having a Whale of a Time. Stories, pictures, songs about whales/large fish should set the scene for this sheet. The stories of Jonah and Pinocchio are both enjoyed by most children. Attention can focus on the use of descriptive writing and appropriate adjectives can be displayed on the word tree.

Sheet 33 - Finding Pharaoh. There are excellent books and pictures depicting the Ancient Egyptians and the pharaohs. (The most recent is in the BBC Fact Finder Series - highly recommended!) Initial descriptions can be taken from this sheet, further descriptive writing can be based on research from other sources. The story element can be based on speculations about the life of the pharaohs, the pyramid/tomb builders, the reasons for the objects buried in the tomb and events surrounding them.

Sheet 34 - Help Mummy! From the historical to the world of Hammer films. 'The Curse of the Mummy'. If you decide to dramatise the event remember to keep the first-aid box locked or you will lose all the bandages!

Sheet 35 - When I grow up. Discussions of possibilities, preferred occupations and potential locations can lead to the questions of what kind of person will you become? - character, caring, friendly, etc., how do you demonstrate friendship? Will you be healthy? Displays to support this sheet should provide an appropriate range of role models from ethnic minorities and women as well as white males.

Sheet 36 - Christmas is Coming. This sheet offers a whole range of potential uses. At its simplest it can be a description of Santa Claus, his personality, work, life, adventures, etc., but it can also be used in a broader sense. An imaginary party can be planned with lists of guests, presents, games to be played. The writing can be predictive of what may happen on Christmas day.

The children can be asked to write a sad/happy Christmas story or a what if ... story 'The Christmas Eve Santa Claus broke his leg'.

Sheet 37 - Up up and away. Children can write an account of their journey to the place they would most like to visit (for a holiday, to live, for adventures, etc.). They might then be given a second blank sheet and be told that their balloon blew off-course and they arrived at the destination they would least like. The result of the writing may well offer powerful insights into children's understanding or attitudes to certain parts of the world: USA, Black Africa, India, France, etc. Such insights should inform future work, displays and resources in order to challenge stereotypes.

Sheet 38 - Magic Carpet. The Magic Carpet can transport you to faraway places (in time and space.) The choice of who will go and what will be taken ought to be supported by explanations of why. Thus connections should be made between where you go and what you take.

The sheet can be preceded by role play on the carpet - the magic carpet. Stories can be acted out (link to sheets 46-8) and characters, plot and props all decided.

Sheet 39 - Look Out. Linked to safety education this sheet can be used as a catalyst for serious discussions of dangers around us. The child writes about what happens next and this allows a very wide choice ranging from for example the intervention of the adult to prevent the accident to for example total mayhem followed by the activities of the emergency services and a fight for life.

Sheet 40 - Chef's Delight. Once again a wide range of options is available here. The sheet can be a menu, realistic or quite fanciful. It can be a serious attempt to design an imagined meal, perhaps a special occasion or just a domestic everyday affair. The children can be asked to work to a budget, to consider health factors, fast food, etc.

Displays which include pictures and books showing cafes, restaurants, meals and menus should be provided. Some schools have had considerable success with mini-enterprises based on cafes and the sheet would be helpful in the planning and execution of such a task.

Best foot forward

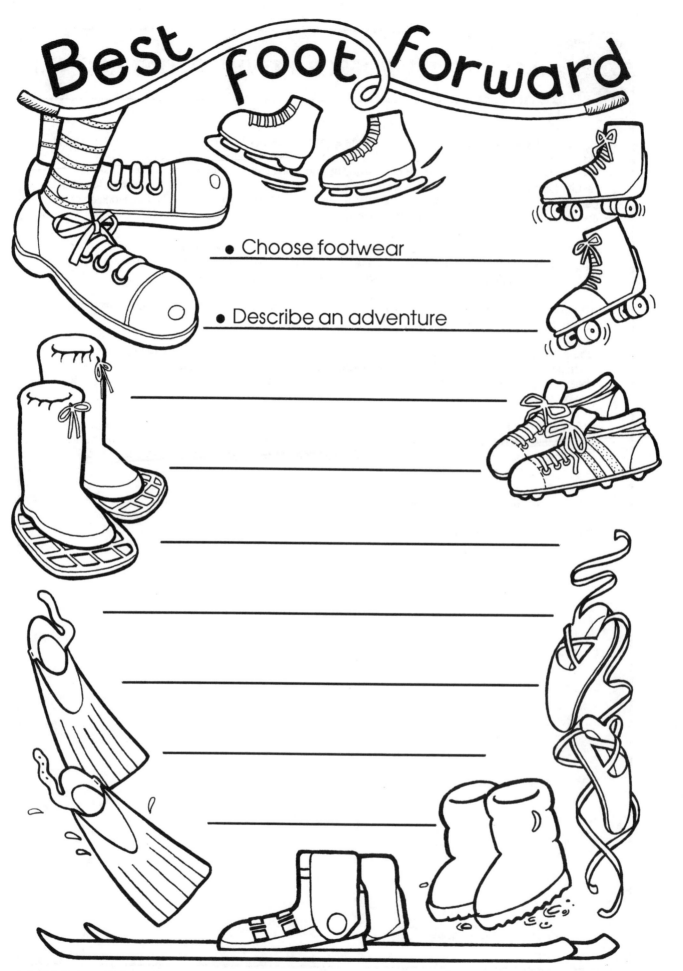

- Choose footwear _____
- Describe an adventure _____

_____

_____

_____

_____

_____

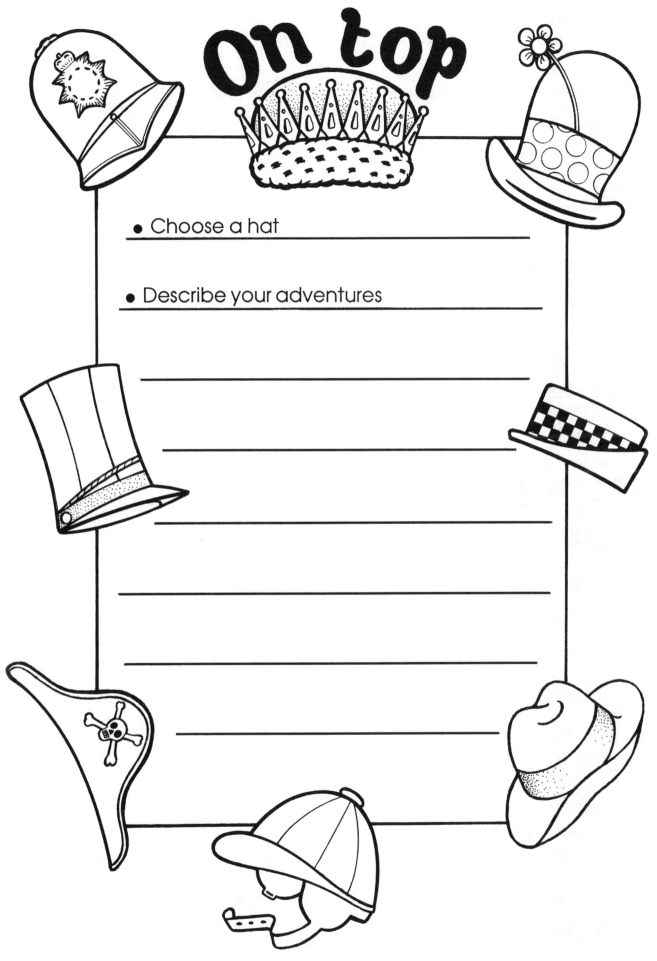

On top

- Choose a hat _____

- Describe your adventures _____

_____

_____

_____

_____

_____

Having a whale of a time

- Describe what happens next.

Finding Pharaoh

- Describe a pharaoh's tomb.

_____

_____

_____

- What happened next?

When I grow up

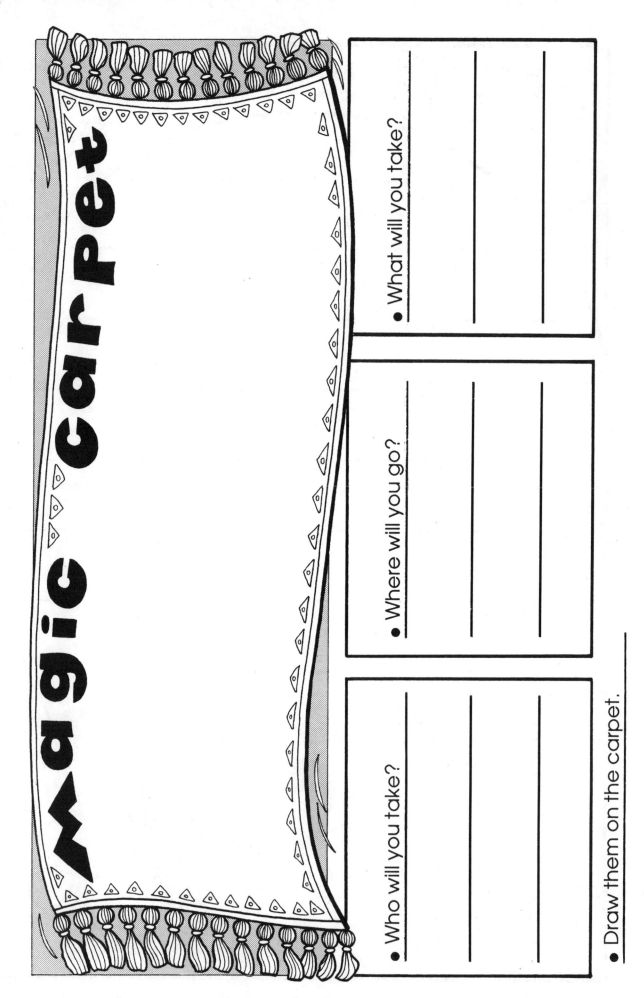

Magic Carpet

- What will you take?

- Where will you go?

- Who will you take?

- Draw them on the carpet.

LOOK OUT!

● Describe what happens next.

_____

_____

_____

_____

_____

_____

Chef's Delight

FUN WITH WORDS

This section encourages the children to play with words, to experiment with letters and sounds and to think about some of the idiosyncracies of the English language. Group and dictionary work can be encouraged throughout.

Individual Sheets

Sheet 42 - Fill the Space. The challenge is to retain the first and last letters but to find alternative middles all of which should form real words. E.g. weed, wood, word, ward, wand, wild, wind, etc.
In the second example the first two letters remain constant and the word is formed by adding the final two letters. E.g. stop, stay, step, stun, star, stab, etc. Finally the centre of the word is fixed and the first and last letters should be added. E.g. hood, food, pool, fool, cool, tool, moon, soon, etc.

Sheet 43 - How many words? The list starts with 'tell' and one letter is changed each time. The only stipulation is that a 'real' word should be formed each time.
When this is done by a group each child can take turns in providing a word. This activity also works well on screen. Which group can produce the largest printout?
How many of the words on the list can be contained within a single sentence? a paragraph? a story?

Sheet 44 - Changing Words. These word games are more demanding. One letter is changed each time in order to move from the first to the last word but the intermediate steps must also be 'real' words. Solutions, e.g.

cat	toe	pan	hand	can
sat	top	pin	band	fan
sit	tap	pit	bank	fun
sip	cap	fit	bark	fur

Sheet 45 - Handwork. The link word is 'hand'. Having matched text to pictures the children should try to explain what the phrases actually mean (verbally/in writing).
The literal meanings, suitably interpreted, can be great fun. This theme is continued in the two junior books in this series.

Early Play Writing

A.T.1. Level 1
Participate as speakers and listeners in group activities, including imaginative play.

Level 2
Participate as speakers and listeners in a group engaged in a given task.

Role play can lead to discussion of what a 'play' is. Characters develop from the parts played 'I'm a chef', 'I'm a doctor'. What should we wear, carry, do, say in order to be like the character?

Individual Sheets

Sheet 46 - Play Writer. An outline plan. What shall we 'play'?
Who is to be part of the activity? What clothes and other objects are needed?
This can best be achieved through group discussion and draft planning.

Sheet 47 - Storyline. The action can simply be talked and acted through. As it develops it will be appropriate to write down the storyline (plot), with a beginning, a middle and an end.

Sheet 48 - The Script. The script itself can be viewed as guidance only.
The children can discuss whether a script has to be exact and learned by heart or whether it can be a rough guide, the words being of less importance than the plot.

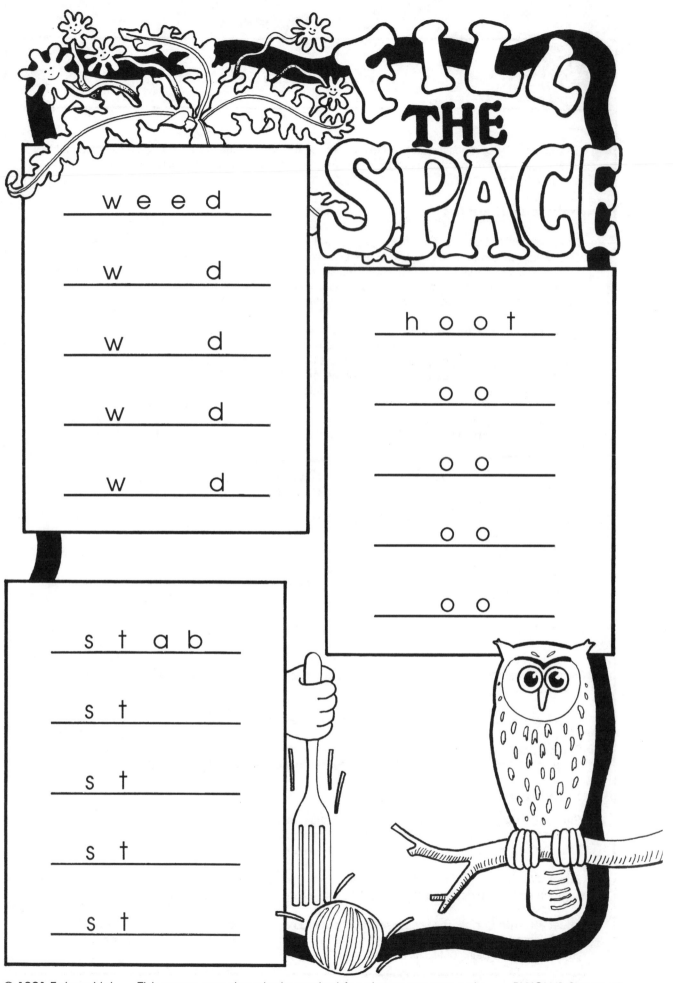

FILL THE SPACE

w e e d

w _ _ d

w _ _ d

w _ _ d

w _ _ d

h o o t

_ o o _

_ o o _

_ o o _

_ o o _

s t a b

s t _ _

s t _ _

s t _ _

s t _ _

HOW MANY WORDS?

tell _____

_____

_____

_____

Work with a friend.

Change one

letter each time.

_____

_____

_____

_____

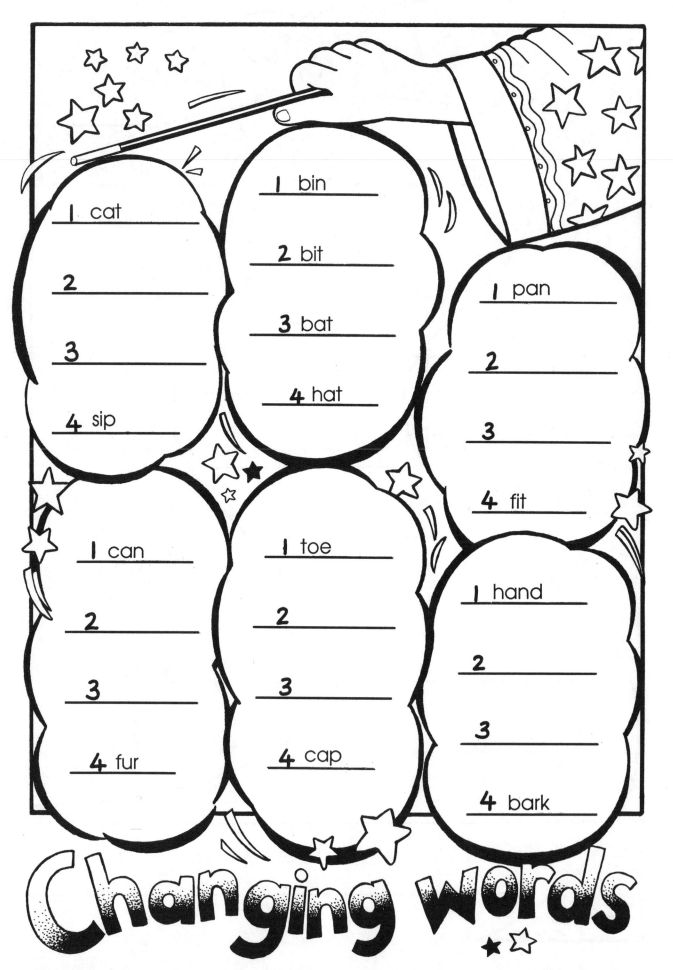

1 cat

2 ____

3 ____

4 sip

1 bin

2 bit

3 bat

4 hat

1 pan

2 ____

3 ____

4 fit

1 can

2 ____

3 ____

4 fur

1 toe

2 ____

3 ____

4 cap

1 hand

2 ____

3 ____

4 bark

Changing words

Handwork

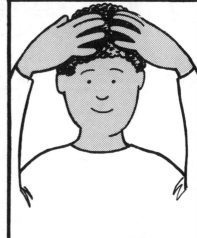

- Match the words

to the pictures

Lend me a hand.

Hand on.

Hand round.

Shake hands.

Handmade.

Handout.

Hands up.

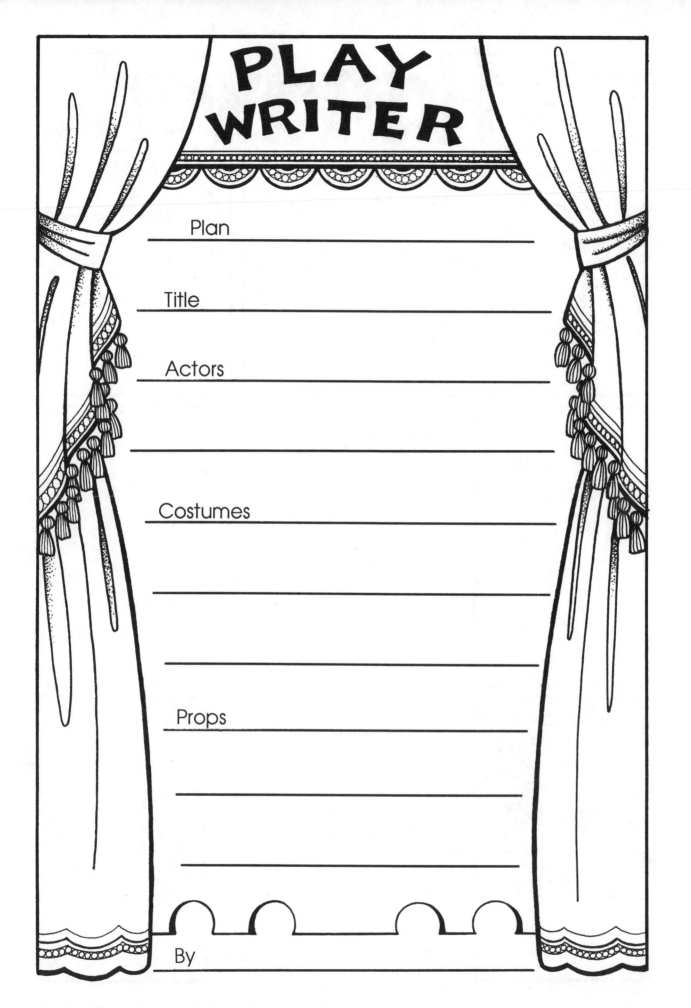

PLAY WRITER

Plan

Title

Actors

Costumes

Props

By

BWCW1 Sheet 46

STORYLINE

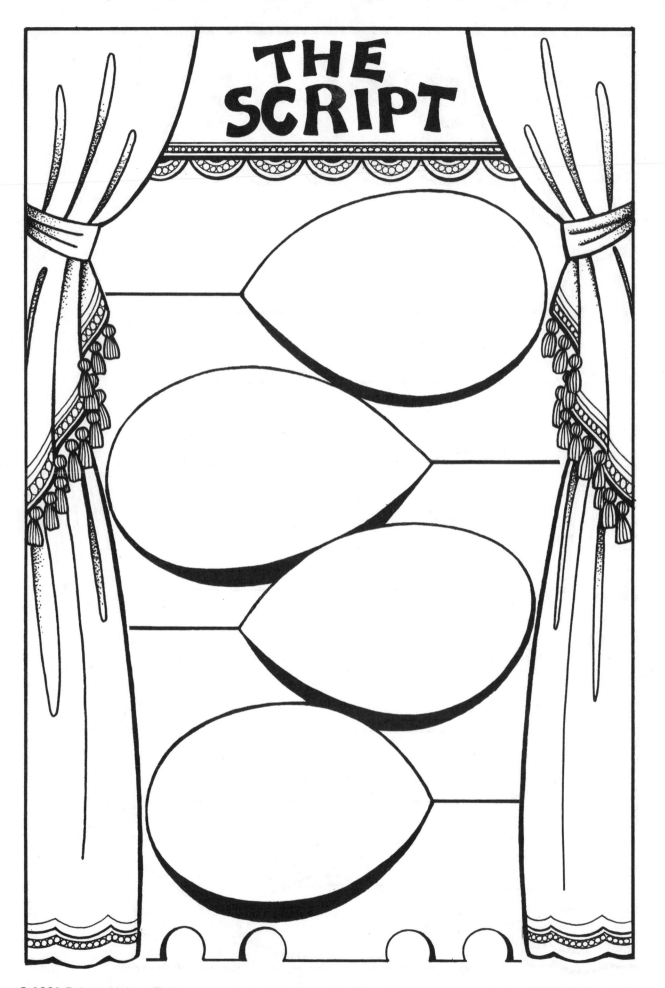

THE SCRIPT